MANCALA

BOARD GAMES

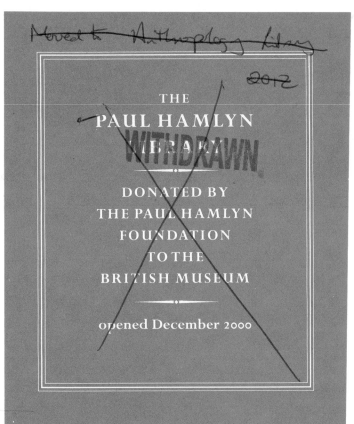

Nigerian 2 × 6 mancala board with a projection in the shape of a human head (cat. 26).

MANCALA

· ·

BOARD GAMES

ALEXANDER J. DE VOOGT

Published for the Trustees of the British Museum by
BRITISH MUSEUM PRESS

794. 074 VOO

© 1997 The Trustees of the British Museum
Published by British Museum Press
A division of the British Museum Company Ltd
46 Bloomsbury Street, London WC1B 3QQ
First published in 1997
British Library Cataloguing in Publication Data
A catalogue record for this book is available from the British Library
ISBN 0-7141-2536-9
Designed by Roger Davies
Printed in Great Britain by Cambridge University Press
Published with the support of

IIAS
International Institute for Asian Studies

HALF-TITLE PAGE
The semi-finals of the Zanzibar Bao Masters Championships, 1994.
(Photo: Author)

BELOW
Crocodile-shaped board from Nigeria (see fig. 27)

CONTENTS

● ●

FOREWORD

• •

THE 1990 British Museum exhibition 'Board Games of the World' was instrumental in drawing attention to the Museum's extensive collections of game boards. Stimulated by this interest, steady progress has since been made in developing and researching the collections in this area.

The popular appeal and simple beauty of such pieces as the red lacquered Chinese mancala board (pl. 4) displayed in that exhibition generated considerable enthusiasm, both from within the Museum and from members of the public. The initial impetus for this book came from Irving Finkel, the exhibition's curator, who introduced Alex de Voogt to the Ethnography Department and suggested the publication of its mancala collection.

Since 1990 the Ethnography Department has been fortunate in being able to acquire a substantial number of mancala boards from Asia, an area previously neglected in the field of mancala research. The decision to publish boards from this region as well as examples from the Middle East and the West Indies has provided an excellent opportunity for the examination and discussion of the great variety of styles, shapes and physical characteristics of the boards, as well as the diversity of playing rules in this widely distributed game.

Change is highlighted as a key theme of the book, as witnessed by the evolving shape of the holes, outlines and exterior contours of mancala boards and, most significantly, by the gradual physical changes caused by intensive play. Many of the boards in the collection show signs of considerable wear, in their surface patina, the deep grooves formed by fingers, or, in some instances, the holes produced by repeated play. There are also examples of prestigious ceremonial boards and even examples produced for the tourist market which, owing to the small size of their holes or their rather fanciful shapes, prove impossible to play on.

In this catalogue Dr de Voogt presents an imaginative and challenging interpretation of the mancala boards in the Ethnography Department of the British Museum. We hope it will serve to generate further interest in this fascinating game.

JULIE HUDSON
Department of Ethnography, British Museum

Boat-shaped mancala board from Sierra Leone, supported at each end by a standing figure (cat. 44)

ACKNOWLEDGEMENTS

● ●

THIS study was made possible through the financial support of the International Institute for Asian studies, Research School CNWS and funds for affiliated research in New York (AMNH Collection Study Grant), Zanzibar and Barbados (Society for the Advancement of Research in the Tropics, CGD). I wish to thank David Agar, Matthew Charles, Imogen Laing, Saul Peckham, Mike Row, Ros Walford and my father for their efforts and help, and in particular Mike Cobb, who assisted me in many ways from the very start. I would also like to thank Hans Rashbrook for his drawings, Teresa Francis and Delia Pemberton for their patience in editing the text, and John Mack for special permission to produce this catalogue.

Without the help and friendship of my colleagues and the many players of Bao and Warri this study would not have been possible. I need to thank Irving Finkel, who suggested this project in the first place and whose endless support and contacts have made it such a pleasant undertaking. I owe particular thanks to Lucien Reurich, whose comments and insights were so fundamental, and to Julie Hudson, whose energy and efforts were inspiring and who helped me to be patient and to bring the task to a successful completion. I am also very grateful to Roslyn Walker, Laurence Russ and Vernon Eagle for their valuable suggestions and to many others who have created the foundations of the mancala research field. Finally, I thank the players of Speightstown, Bridgetown and Stonetown who taught me the players' perspective and showed me the joy of mancala board games.

ALEXANDER J. DE VOOGT

PREFACE

● ●

MANCALA games have been studied from many different perspectives. This study focuses on the collection of mancala boards in the Ethnography Department of the British Museum, which provides an excellent basis from which to analyse and discuss previously neglected aspects of these games. After presenting a brief history of mancala research and the development of the game, it will concentrate on the significance of the playing materials in terms of physical change. Thus the focus shifts from the context in which the game is played to the changing shape of the boards, their weight and sound, even the effects of wear caused by intensive play. Through careful examination of such characteristics it becomes possible to trace the life cycle of a mancala board, enabling us to approach an assessment of the aesthetic qualities it acquires in the process.

The theme of change extends not only to the mancala boards themselves, but to the rules by which mancala games are played. As these change and develop, certain stratagems may in turn affect the shape of the boards, once again illustrating the fluid character of mancala as the emphasis moves from context to object and back again. It is hoped that this shift in perspective will change the reader's mind in the same way that mancala has changed the minds of so many involved in its research.

Map of the world showing the places of origin of the mancala boards in the British Museum collection. (Drawing: Hans Rashbrook)

1

M A N C A L A
Changing the perspective

T H E history of the origin and subsequent development of mancala is obscure. The study of Asian mancala has been largely neglected and the mancala games played in the Middle East and North Africa have not yet been examined in detail, while the few ancient boards mentioned in the literature do not significantly extend present knowledge of the history, development and spread of the game. Nonetheless, the British Museum collection, with its nineteenth-century examples from Africa and Asia and its recently acquired boards from Asia, the Middle East and the West Indies, goes some way towards illustrating the history of individual boards and demonstrating the broader physical and geographical distinctions to be observed among these fascinating objects.

Mancala, also written 'mankala' or 'manqala', has characteristic physical and playing features. In the past, depending on the perspective of research, either the physical (game boards) or the playing (game rules) characteristics have been stressed. In this context, it is interesting to note the following definitions from an art-historical and an anthropological study respectively:

Mankala (also spelled *mancala*) is a 'count and capture' (or strategy) boardgame that is played by two people or, on rare occasions, by two teams on a board containing two, three, or four parallel rows of cuplike depressions or 'holes'. It is played with a predetermined number of identical counters or 'pieces'. The goal is to capture the majority of the pieces. (Walker 1990)

Mankala (from *naqala*; root -*qala* [*sic*] = transfer, move things about) is the Arabic name now conventionally used to denote a whole genre of boardgames prevalent in Africa and parts of Asia, in which identical seeds are sown around

1 Ethiopian three-row folding mancala board (cat. 4).

lineal or circular formations of holes in an attempt to immobilise or annihilate the other player(s) by the capture of his/her/their seeds. (Townshend 1986)

Mancala games are often classified according to their number of rows. Two-row games are the most common, three-row games are primarily found in Ethiopia, and four-row games are found mostly on the East African coast. They are known by a great variety of names, which may refer to the material of the board, the playing pieces, the moves, the context or even the sound of play. Deledicq and Popova (1977) distinguished Wari and Solo as the most common names for two-row and four-row mancala in Africa. The word 'Wari' has many variants: Ouri (Cape Verde), Ouré (Senegal), Wouri (Mali), Ware (Sudan, Togo, Gambia), Wari (Senegal, Haiti), Woro (Gambia), Warri (Sierra Leone, Togo, Barbados), Wawi (Antilles), Awari (Surinam), Awèlè (Ivory Coast) and Owela (Angola) (see also Santos Silva 1995, p. 37; Murray 1952). Similar lists exist for Solo (Chisolo, Luzolo, Soro) and other common names: Adji (Ayo, Aji, Agi, Adito, Adjika, Adjiboto), Mancala (Mangala, Mankala, Mangola) and Bao (Bau, Mbau, Mbo).

Some of these names are distinct terms, but others just represent differences in transcription or cognates in other languages. It is difficult to establish the true origin of any name, since each group of players is likely to have its own theories for the origin of its adopted version. Walker (1990, p. 121) states that Warri was named after a town in Nigeria or taken from the Ghanaian word for 'far', a reference to the endless moves in the game. There is even a kingdom named Warri south of the Kingdom of Benin (see Ayomíke 1993). Likewise, 'Bao' in Swahili refers to a wooden board, but 'Solo' is both a Pemba Swahili word for the playing seeds and a general word for the game in other African languages.

The names for the playing pieces invite similar comparisons and create similar confusion. 'Kete' in Swahili refers to the cowrie shells originally used as playing pieces, although modern players use seeds from the *Caesalpinia Bonduc* bush: 'komwe' – probably the original Swahili name for this seed – is only used for special expressions in the game. Mancala has been compared to war, trade and numerous other situations in which goods or people change hands, resulting in the pieces being called soldiers, cows, money, prisoners or wives. The rows of the board, the individual holes, the special end holes or enlarged holes are also individually named: in Kédang (East Indonesia), for instance, each hole is called after a particular body part (Barnes 1975). The sound of play is also relevant: the Vai (Liberia) are said to have named their mancala game 'Kpo' after the characteristic repetitive percussion sound made when pieces are spread on to the board.

Mancala has only recently received due attention as a research topic: although the first person to use mancala as a generic term was Culin (1893), it was not until Deledicq and Popova (1977) that a complete book was dedicated to the subject. In the last ten years, however, previously little-known mancala games have been the subject of three doctoral theses (Townshend 1986, Walker 1990, de Voogt 1995a) and other extensive studies (Retschitzki 1990, Santos Silva 1995 and Russ 1984). There has also been a change within the study of mancala itself: earlier general studies (e.g. Béart 1955, Murray 1952, Bell 1960, Deledicq and Popova 1977) are now used as introductions to the more specialised recent studies written from art-historical, psychological, pedagogical and anthropological perspectives. An important observation in these studies is the paucity of information relating to Asian games, an area expected to prove fundamental in developing a better understanding of the history and distribution of mancala.

The beginnings of mancala are still debated, though it is generally believed to have originated in either Asia or Africa. Analogies with its spread have been found in the travels of Muslim pilgrims, Arab merchants and Asian voyager-colonists, but although considerable evidence has been accumulated to support various theories, no agreement has yet been reached (see Townshend 1986, Walker 1990). Further archaeological evidence and anthropological research (e.g. Townshend 1977a/b) could be useful in resolving the questions surrounding the origins and history of mancala.

Museums started collecting wooden mancala boards no earlier than 1823. The British Museum, which only obtained its first piece in the 1860s

2 The oldest board in the British Museum collection: a boat-shaped 2 × 6 wooden board from Sierra Leone, collected in the 1860s (cat. 36).

(fig. 3) now has the most extensive collection in the world. Although Roslyn Walker's catalogue of sculptured mancala boards from sub-Saharan Africa (1990) only describes thirty-six British Museum pieces, less than half the actual number in the collection, these still outnumber the holdings of most museums, few of which possess more than twenty boards. Not surprisingly, the largest collections of African mancala boards are to be found in the national museums of former colonial powers, such as the Musée de l'Homme in Paris (France), the Museum für Völkerkunde in Hamburg (Germany) and the Musée Royal de l'Afrique Centrale in Tervuren (Belgium). Smaller collections can be found in other museums in Germany, England, Switzerland and the United States. The only significant collection of boards in Africa is probably that of the National Museum in Lagos, Nigeria, from which eight boards are described in Walker's catalogue.

The great majority of these African boards – approximately eighty per cent – are of West African origin, mainly from Liberia, Nigeria, Sierra Leone and the Ivory Coast, with some examples from Ethiopia, Tanzania and Zaire. Of the 434 boards described in Walker's catalogue, 417 are made of wood, six of metal, four of palm rib, three of pottery, two of clay and one of animal dung. A board from Zambia made of corrugated iron has since added to this list of materials. The Asian boards in the

PLATE 1 Red and gold painted board in the form of a stylised dragon supported on four legs and terminating in upright animal heads. Indonesia (cat. 84).
PLATE 2 Wheelbarrow board from Sierra Leone (cat. 43).
PLATE 3 Unusual 2 × 3 + 2 Javanese mancala board with legs and carved animal-head terminals. The holes are painted alternately in red and green. Indonesia (cat. 82).

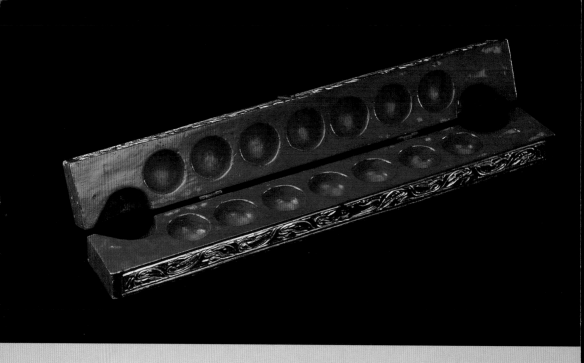

British Museum collection include examples in ivory and lacquered wood.

Furthermore, archaeological evidence from Africa has yielded ancient examples of stone, metal and pottery boards that provide significant information on the history and antiquity of mancala. With the exception of certain stone boards in Egypt, all archaeological discoveries in natural rock or stone have proved difficult to date. Boards found in the area of Great Zimbabwe suggest that some date from at latest the nineteenth century, while other examples in Zaire, Angola and Ghana may date from the sixth century or earlier. An oval pottery board from Mali has been analysed using modern techniques and found to date back to the twelfth or thirteenth century. It is tempting to claim that mancala is the oldest board game in the world, but this can neither be proved nor disproved with the data presently available, since the Mali piece and the Egyptian examples were not necessarily used to play mancala games.

Modern anthropological evidence reveals that Asian mancala is played mostly by women and children, while in Africa it is played predominantly by men. Rules in Asia have, in general, been less complicated and diverse than those in Africa, suggesting an African origin. Townshend (1986) argued that four-row mancala had to be of African origin since it did not even occur in Asia, but subsequent research has shown that it also occurs in Sri Lanka and China. More evidence remains to be gathered on the

3 A rare board from Chad with a 4 × 4 configuration (cat. 2).

PLATE 4 Red lacquered folding board with gold-decorated plant design on the outside. China (cat. 71).

PLATE 5 Polychrome decorated board supported at the corners by four equestrian figures and at the centre by a kneeling female figure holding a child. Nigeria (cat. 28).

games played in the Middle East and on the Indian subcontinent: anthropological research looks most promising in this respect.

According to Walker (1990) the earliest physical evidence of two-row mancala dates from the third century in Sri Lanka, the fourth century in Cyprus, and the sixth century in Ethiopia. Evidence for three-row games is difficult to assess, as they are easily confused with the ancient Egyptian game of *senet*; however, a three-row board does appear on an eighteenth-century statue from Zaire (fig. 10). Four-row mancala was first mentioned by Flacourt in 1658, but some confusion still exists as to the oldest example of a four-row board.

It was several centuries after the development of mancala in Africa and Asia that it was introduced to the Americas and Europe via the slave trade. The two-row games known in West Africa were taken to the New World and played in the Caribbean islands and the northern parts of South America perhaps as early as the sixteenth century. Mancala is now played as far north as the Bahamas, on most islands of the Caribbean, and perhaps as far south as Brazil, though literature on this subject is limited (Herskovits 1934). Syrian immigrants are said to have introduced the game to New York, where it was spotted by Culin (1893). Indeed, immigrants have often been responsible for introducing mancala to new environments: other examples include Haitians in the Bahamas, and Filipinos in Guam.

In Europe, only the Muslims in Spain and the inhabitants of Cyprus and the Cyclades originally played forms of mancala, but several commercial attempts have since been made to introduce some simple two-row variants to Western Europe and the United States. Plain Wari boards are found in department stores and some fancier boards have been designed in California. Even in Barbados a commercial attempt has been made to make the local 'Warri' game more popular. It is notable that the more complicated variants, like the four-row games, are seldom played outside their region of origin.

The future of mancala research lies partly in the study of other museum collections, since so little attention has been given to the Asian and American mancala boards. This study aims to highlight the aesthetic and artistic qualities of mancala boards in general, and should facilitate the

18

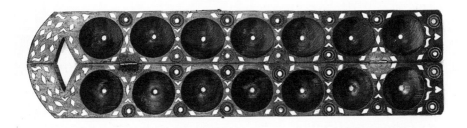

4 Syrian 2 × 7 folding mancala boards: *(top)* unfinished wood; *(centre)* wood inlaid with mother-of-pearl; *(bottom)* plain varnished wood (cat. 100-2).

appreciation of other museum collections. Research would be greatly served by a proper index of mancala boards, especially those of Asian origin. China, India, Indonesia, Malaysia, the Maldive Islands, the Philippines, Sri Lanka, Syria, Antigua and Barbados are among the many countries whose museum collections of mancala boards were unpublished or unknown prior to this study. The Asian, Caribbean and Middle Eastern collections of other museums have not yet received sufficient attention, although recent research at the American Museum of Natural History (New York) revealed a dozen boards from Asia, Africa and South America not mentioned in previous studies.

Mancala research now has a sound base from which to develop. Mancala is slowly receiving serious attention from many disciplines. Wari programs have been written for computers, and the British Museum is expanding, researching and exhibiting its extensive collection of mancala boards. An increase in presentations at colloquia and recent publications also testify to this growing general interest.

At the same time, in some places competition from chess, draughts and dominoes threatens the existence of mancala, while economic factors do not always allow for recreational play. Rituals slowly disappear through cultural change, and attempts at the commercial introduction of the game have never been very successful, since it is so easy to create a home-made playing board. However, there are many reasons for mancala to survive. It can be played anywhere, its rules are simple yet endlessly stimulating, and it readily becomes a pleasant addiction for all ages, as the number of books and boards available will show. There are many futures for mancala. There are many ways of looking at the game. This study is just one of them.

2
MANCALA
PLAYING RULES
The art of the game

MANCALA rules, though simple, are complicated to explain. Essentially, play consists of one basic movement which involves 'sowing' and 'capturing' playing pieces, or 'seeds', using a board comprising rows of holes. Each move causes multiple changes in the position of the pieces on the board; if multiple sowings and captures are allowed, these changes become even more difficult to calculate. In the case of Sungka, played in the Philippines, these multiple sowings tend to continue a long time before the move is finished. The calculations involved are so complex that players do not bother to make them; thus the outcome of the game is usually a surprise. More serious games, such as Omweso in Uganda (Nsimbi 1968), demand considerable skill since the capturing rules are quite complicated. Bao, the most complicated of all, includes various direction changes, multiple captures and sowings and, according to Townshend (1986), the highest average turnover of seeds per move.

Even the most basic rule of play results in multiple changes on the board, and this mutational complexity is what makes the championship games like Wari and Bao so difficult for humans but relatively simple for computers (see Allis et al. 1991, de Voogt 1995a). The art of these games is the calculation of multiple changes, a prerequisite for all masters since strategies can only be executed once this skill has been acquired. The feats of memory necessary to become a Bao master are considerable and quite different from those needed in chess, where relatively few changes occur

5 Ugandan boys playing a local form of mancala (Omweso). (Photo from J. Roscoe, *The Baganda: an Account of their Native Customs and Beliefs*, London 1911, p. 78).

per move. The ultimate challenge in this respect is a game of blind Bao. Abdulrahim M. Foum showed this skill at a colloquium in 1995 (de Voogt 1995b, p. 2) when he played forty-four moves with his back to the board, calculating the moves mentally and communicating them verbally.

The playing rules of mancala games were first described by Flacourt, who in 1658 presented a brief summary of a Madagascan game called 'Fifangha'. Murray's (1952) catalogue of rules introduced useful terminology to index the rules and compare variations from all over the world; however, it omits to mention the continuous changes and developments to which they are subject. This mutability is the most typical feature of mancala playing rules.

In Africa, even when playing the complicated four-row variants, the players simply learn new rules as and when they occur and develop their skill by playing as often as possible. In Bao, for example, some situations in the game occur so rarely that even masters may disagree about the rules governing them. In the case of two players from different towns following different rules, they will agree which variant they are going to adopt before playing. This continuous process of consensus and adjustment has led to a natural and gradual development of rules; if the players change their minds, the rules change accordingly.

The rules of mancala games are as diverse as their players. Apart from a curious exception in China, mancala games are played with identical playing pieces which are spread on to the board in a circular movement, usually anticlockwise. These movements result in two main families of mancala games (see also Eagle 1995, p. 50): those in which the players have their own rows into which they spread their pieces (the four-row games) and those in which they share rows (the two-row and three-row games).

6 Four-row wooden board supported on stones, used by the Venda people. South Africa. (Photo from H. Stayt, *The Bavenda*, London 1931, pl. XLVIII).

A two-row game, Wari, is one of the most widespread mancala games in the world. Its rules are relatively simple, though local variations illustrate the continuously changing nature of the game. Wari's strength lies in its uncomplicated rules and excellent potential for competitive play: it is played in both computer contests and master championships. The Wari board consists of two rows of six holes. At the start of the game, each hole contains four pieces, usually seeds. There are two players, each of whom 'owns' the row of six holes closest to him/her. One player starts by taking up all four seeds from any one hole on his/her side of the board and spreads or 'sows' them one by one into each consecutive hole, moving in an anti-clockwise direction. The other player follows suit. Play proceeds by alternate turns, each turn consisting of one such spreading. Any number of seeds can be played, the object of the game being to capture the most seeds. Captures are made when the last seed of a spreading lands in one of the holes on the opponent's side of the board, bringing the total of seeds in that hole to two or three. When this happens, all the seeds in the hole are taken out of play and added to the player's captured seeds. Furthermore, any seeds from an unbroken sequence of holes containing two or three seeds on the opponent's side immediately preceding the first captured seeds are also captured, making it possible to capture an entire row of seeds in one move. This important rule increases the possibility of multiple captures, which probably contributes to the game's popularity. When no more seeds are left in play, the game is over and the captured seeds are counted (see also Ballou 1978, Béart 1955, Russ 1984, pp.14-18).

There are numerous variations on these rules, for instance using more or fewer holes per row, adding end holes, capturing on an empty hole or end hole, capturing on the opposite or adjacent hole, and so on. Spreading may take place not only in an anticlockwise direction, but also clockwise or in both directions. Other combinations of seeds may be used in the starting position; multiple captures or multiple spreadings may be allowed; captures may be limited by empty holes or end holes. Players may start with or without all the seeds in the game, take out captured seeds, reuse captured seeds within the game or redistribute captured seeds until no seeds are left for one player. They may change the initial set-up, alter

7 Warri board from Antigua, West Indies (cat. 103).

the rules, or introduce special holes such as end holes, reverse holes, 'houses' or enlarged holes, and holes containing specific numbers of seeds. They may disallow captures of all the opponent's holes at once or outlaw the capture of special holes. There are even occasions when more than two players (usually teams) can participate.

Local variants may also occur. For example, in Speightstown, a town in the north of Barbados, a player wins a game by 'cutting', or capturing, twenty-five, i.e. the majority, of the seeds in the game. If the game ends because one player has no seeds left with which to play, the seeds on the board remain there and do not count towards the total captured seeds of either player. In the capital, Bridgetown, however, the seeds remaining on the board are split between the two players. If there is an odd number of seeds, the extra one goes to the player with the most seeds on his side of the board. In this version, it is enough to capture twenty-four seeds, since in practice there are always one or two seeds left on the board towards the end of the game. To this day, the two towns disagree on this issue, while concurring that cutting twenty-five is more difficult and will result in more draws than when cutting twenty-four.

Rules often become more complicated in championships, demonstrating an ongoing refinement. The difficulties that arise can be extreme, particularly in the case of Bao, where entire chapters have been dedicated to the subject of championship rules (Townshend 1986, pp. 114-23; de Voogt

1995, pp. 35-44). Championship rules do not only refer to the moving of the pieces but to the number of games in a match, the decision on who will start the game, the punishment (or reward) for cheating, the treatment of guests in a players' club, and the conduct of spectators.

Ceremonial, recreational, women's, and children's games all have different sets of rules. In Barbados, for instance, the children's game – usually called 'rounders' – features multiple sowings, captures dependent on position rather than number and captures on both sides of the board, but not the multiple captures found in the adult game.

All these rules have little influence on the shape of the board. Only minor adjustments are needed to play Wari on a 2×7 board instead of a 2×6, and many games and variations can be played on one and the same board. Though there are few cases where the rules have influenced the shape of the board, there is one notable example in which a complication in the rules has affected the shape of the holes. In two-row Wari, four-row Bao and many other games (Odeleye 1977, p. 23; de Voogt 1995a) building a 'house' of many seeds is an important stratagem in the game. This requires the playing holes or 'cups' to be big enough to hold up to twenty seeds at one time. A good playing board therefore provides the appropriate

8 Malawi Bao board with characteristic enlarged houses in the centre of the board (cat. 20).

9 Bao board. Tanzania (cat. 17).

size of holes. In the case of Sungka, there are seven cowrie shells in each of the 2 × 7 holes. However, since the cowrie shells are smaller than the Caesalpinia Bonduc seeds used elsewhere, these boards do not need to be very large.

Another example of game rules affecting the shape of the board can be found in Bao and some of its variants, which have fixed places for their houses. These houses, which frequently reach a considerable size, have many roles associated with them. Each player 'owns' one such house on his/her side of the board, where it usually appears as a square hole between rows of round cups. The fight for this house is sometimes referred to as 'kitakomwe', 'komwe' being the term for the seeds used in play (see above). Roslyn Walker (personal communication) observed a board in which two additional holes on each side of the board were also enlarged. In Bao, these holes – the penultimate holes on either side of the board – are referred to as 'kimbi'. The special game known as 'kitakimbi' refers to the battle for these holes that takes place once they have acquired many seeds; this position on the board is frequently difficult to defend. Thus even the stratagems of a game can influence the eventual appearance of the board on which it is played. They are therefore significant not only for the masters who play, but also and to a lesser extent for the makers of the boards.

3
MANCALA PLAYING BOARDS
From context to object

MANCALA has received much attention in the last ten years in terms of its social and/or cultural significance. However, once mancala boards are removed from their original setting and placed in museums, valuable contextual information may be lost. Early museum records rarely provide sufficient detail to reconstruct accurately a board's cultural significance. Only a board that has been photographed or filmed in its original setting before being brought to a museum (as has happened in some rare instances) comes with the necessary evidence to define its proper context.

Nonetheless, boards in museum collections possess many interesting features that can shed light both on the identity of their previous owners and on the purpose of the game. Close examination of these special features changes the focus from the cultural setting to the boards themselves: the size of holes in a board, its weight or even its sound suddenly become relevant. Before discussing these features, however, it is necessary to differentiate between ritual and recreational boards.

The literature on mancala (e.g. Walker 1990) ascribes either a recreational or a ritual purpose to the game. Ritual contexts include weddings, funerals, divination and ceremonies such as the selection or installation of a new ruler. In Uganda, for example, the Ganda king was required to play mancala as part of his accession ceremony. Central to this ritual was the act of picking the seeds used as counters in the game. The ability of an experienced mancala player to defeat his opponent with a single reverse move using only a few seeds served as a metaphor for the new ruler's abil-

10 Wooden statue representing
Shyaam aMbul aNgoong, the
founder of the Kuba Kingdom,
Zaire, seated with a 3 × 3
mancala board before him
(cat. 65).

ity to control his people successfully through tact, diplomacy and intellectual maturity. A fine statue in the British Museum (fig. 10) represents the Kuba king Shyaam aMbul aNgoong, who according to oral traditions introduced mancala ('Lyeel') to the Kuba people. Given the numerous inventions and innovations attributed to Shyaam by the Kuba, it is significant that the mancala board carved on the plinth of the statue should have been chosen as the emblem used to identify him. Even in Europe, mancala has played a part in royal ceremony: in 1919 King George V of England received an impressive mancala table from the King of Uganda, Daudi Chwa (fig. 11).

Among mancala collections, royal boards and prestigious gifts stand out because of their size, their use of expensive woods and scarce materials, their fine craftsmanship and sometimes their colour. Most importantly, these boards have remained largely untouched, having been made for display rather than for serious play. Even boards made of more durable

11 Table-shaped 4 × 8 board with pedestal, presented by Daudi Chwa, King of Uganda, to King George V of England (cat. 56).

12 Cuboid folding mancala board from Sri Lanka. Note the minimal-size cups, unsuitable for playing (cat. 95).

materials such as ivory, metal or hard woods are devalued by repeated play: their function is symbolic rather than practical. In particular, such a board symbolises prestige when it changes hands; the more important the exchange, the more prestigious the board. Some boards may have had a purely symbolic function. For example, the Sri Lankan boards acquired by the British Museum in 1898 (see cat. nos 89-99; fig. 12) are too small to use and were probably made for altars as symbols of the game.

Boards used for other rituals, for instance weddings or funerals, do not necessarily have any special characteristics and are therefore indistinguishable from ordinary recreational boards. Descriptions of ceremonies using mancala are scarce, although rituals employing two- and three-row boards have been recorded, mainly in West Africa and Ethiopia. There are also instances of mancala boards being used for divination, which could perhaps explain the number of holes and seeds employed.

Unlike the prestigious boards, boards made for so-called 'recreational' purposes gain value when they are used intensively, since the changes in shape caused by wear create a better playing medium. In Africa, recre-

31

ational mancala games are played predominantly by men, while in Asia, it is more often recorded as a game for women or girls. There are also restrictions on age, with participation in mancala games being restricted to the periods prior to, during, or after puberty. In various parts of Africa, for example, it has formed part of boyhood education, been restricted to the period after circumcision, or treated as an old men's game: this last situation frequently occurs where the game is already in decline.

Elsewhere in Africa, women play other, usually simpler, versions of the game. Bao as played by the Swahili-speaking people (National Museums 1971) and Ayo as played by the Yoruba (Odeleye 1977) have special women's or children's versions. Walker (1990, p. 132) cites that a gender-based difference in the number of end holes used has been recorded in Burkina Faso. In Zanzibar, children and occasionally women play in the sand, while men use boards. It is most unusual to see women and men play against each other, though in West Africa, kings and their wives (or other married couples) have been known to play a rare game of mixed mancala, and in some societies the wives of the sultan may also play.

Special, all-male, playing clubs dedicated to competitive mancala exist in many African countries and among expatriate communities around the world. The standard of play in these clubs is often such that we should speak of masters rather than of recreational players (see half-title page). Among the Bao players of East Africa, on Pemba Island, Zanzibar, the Tanzanian coast and in Barbados there are players for whom the game is central to their aspirations in life. For such men the game is much more than recreation and acquires the role that chess assumes for chess masters (see de Voogt 1995a).

A final group of recreational boards are those produced for the tourist trade. Although these have an ostensible recreational purpose, their design makes them impractical for use. In order to save costs, the boards are made too small, while the playing holes are often machine-made and very small and shallow. There is, however, a good market for folding boards as souvenirs.

Materials

Mancala boards are made from a wide range of materials, the choice of

PLATE 6 Painted door carved in high relief featuring a 2 × 6 + 2 mancala board in its centre. Nigeria (cat. 31).

PLATE 7 *Okega* shrine divided into three tiers: the middle tier includes a mancala board, possibly a metaphor for conquest. Nigeria (cat. 21).

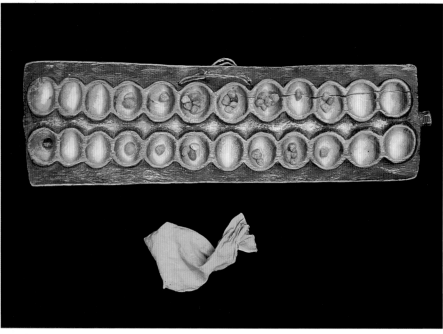

which may be influenced or determined by practical issues, cost, aesthetic considerations or ritual implications. This choice of material – which may be made by the maker, the customer or the player – consequently influences such factors as a board's size, shape, weight and colour, thereby determining to a large extent its physical, playing and aesthetic qualities.

Scooping out holes in the ground to create a simple playing space is probably the oldest way of playing mancala. The practical advantages of this method are manifold: it is inexpensive and requires few (if any) tools, it can readily be made by the players themselves, and it is easily recreated in a different location. Therefore, apart from getting dirty hands, there appears at first to be little reason to choose any other way of playing. However, the prodigious number of mancala boards currently in existence suggests a more significant motivation for their creation.

In some cases, there may be practical difficulties in using the ground. Mancala is played in cities as well as in rural areas and there are obvious practical limitations to creating and recreating large boards in a city centre. Another inconvenient feature of playing mancala in the ground is that the board has continually to be remade after being destroyed by the weather or by vigorous play. In contrast, the use of a tree trunk or root is much more convenient, as wood is not so easily worn or washed away by rain. It is tempting to suggest that mancala boards developed in this way, simple boards dug into the earth leading first to fixed boards and then to portable ones. However, the precise sequence of developments is difficult to determine.

Another element which might provide an explanation for the creation of the boards is amply illustrated by the boards in the British Museum's mancala collection. Unlike holes in the sand, a board can be given as a present. It can be nicely decorated and made into an art object. In other words, a board can develop into something more than mere rows of holes. This distinction, which applies to all the boards in the collection, is most important: when we are looking at a board, we are looking at more than rows of holes.

Wood is the commonest material for mancala boards, but there are also examples made of stone, clay, metal, ivory and palm ribs. The British

PLATE 8 Men playing mancala in the sand. Egypt. (Photo: Chris Spring)
PLATE 9 Mancala board with cup-shaped holes set on to a rectangular base. This separation is further emphasised by the lighter yellow colouring inside the cups. Kenya (cat. 16).

13 Board made from ivory (one half is missing). India (cat. 72).

Museum collection includes pieces worked in relief on a plate of corrugated iron (fig. 16) and pressed into a plaque of dried cow dung (fig. 14). These extraordinary boards are curious but also informative, hinting at the eagerness of the players to engage in a game, as well as to the inventiveness of their makers. Boards created from such readily available materials demonstrate emphatically that mancala is played not only on ceremonial or special occasions but also in places and at times when wood and/or tools may be unavailable but the urge to play remains. Materials such as iron and cow dung are only likely to be used for recreational boards, although their extremely shallow holes suggest impracticality.

Of all these materials, however, wood has the most potential, since it can easily be carved, varnished, polished and shaped into a variety of interesting forms. Wooden boards can also be coloured, although polychrome boards are rare. More commonly, carvings are accentuated by giving them a slightly darker or lighter tone; occasionally, boards are pigmented or have a protective coating. Although limited knowledge of Asian mancala prevents generalisations about this region, the British Museum collection does include examples of coloured boards from Indonesia and a red lacquered Chinese board (see pl. 4).

The wooden boards in the collection range from roughly hewn pieces requiring little technical skill to more sophisticated examples calling for greater craftsmanship and effort. The work and skill expended render such a board more valuable, implying that it could be bought and sold. It might even become a privilege to play on such a board, since the players are not necessarily either the makers or the owners. Wooden boards may also be purchased as gifts or souvenirs, or even to place in museum collections.

Thus there are likely to be differences in craftsmanship between ceremonial boards, popular recreational boards and boards made for the tourist or collectors' market.

Weight is another important factor in the choice of material. Hard woods such as ebony and heavy materials such as metal and stone are far more durable, but require special manufacturing skills and are impractical where the board has to be carried. Nonetheless, archaeological finds of stone, metal and pottery boards have been made at various sites: in Kenya, stone boards carved into the living rock are still being used for play. Portable stone boards are also known and show convincingly the importance of weight: a rare four-row example from Zimbabwe in the American Museum of Natural History weighs 25 kg, yet measures only 57.5 × 37 × 8.5 cm.

Weight also appeared to be a factor when some Makonde (Tanzania) carvers were recently asked by the author to produce a championship-sized Bao board. They did not use the ebony which they favour for making sculptures, since this would have been been both too heavy and too costly; furthermore, finding a large enough piece of ebony for a four-row board appeared rather difficult. Similar factors may account for the scarcity of ivory and metal boards; there are no large examples of these in museum collections, and certainly no four-row boards. India and parts of West

14 Board made from hand-pressed animal dung. Ethiopia (cat. 3).

15 Tree trunk with roughly excavated square holes: the heaviest board in the British Museum collection. Zambia (cat. 69).

Africa are the only places where ivory boards have been discovered; the ivory fragment in the British Museum represents only half of a small two-row board (see fig. 13).

Material and weight also influence the distinctive sound of the boards. While chess is played in complete silence, using pieces mounted on felt to deaden the noise, sound is a distinctive characteristic of mancala. Playing clubs in Africa are renowned for the intense shouting of both players and spectators, while such practices as throwing three or more seeds at a time into adjacent holes in order to speed up the game or slamming the last seed into a full house to enforce superiority over the opponent increases the impression of noise. This simple sound of spreading seeds is central to mancala. Silent earth and strident iron are immediately dismissed by seasoned players; on wood one can hear mistakes in the sowing, and the heavier the wood the lower and warmer the sound during play.

Different qualities again are required for the playing pieces. Seeds are the most popular choice, the best-known variety being the seeds of *Caesalpinia Bonduc* (previously known as *Caesalpinia Christa*), a common shrub that grows on tropical coasts. These come in shades of brown, green, grey or occasionally white, depending on the age and location of the plant; in Antigua, a local orange-red variety adds colour to the board. Though

16 Board made of corrugated iron. Zambia (cat. 68).

not always so colourful, the seeds of the *Caesalpinia Bonduc* are very light, extremely tough and well suited to throwing. Their weight, their smoothness and their perfect size give them qualities similar to those required for a good playing board, while the shine that they often acquire after intensive play also adds to their attractiveness (see pl.15).

Cowrie shells, very common in Asian mancala, also add some colour; in Indonesia plastic cowrie shells are sometimes considered more prestigious than the natural ones. Some boards have sets of pieces made from little stones, pottery fragments, clay balls or marbles. Even iron and ivory pieces in the shape of *Caesalpinia Bonduc* seeds are known. Though it is perfectly possible to play with these pieces, they are not popular because they are often too heavy or too unpleasant to handle.

Form and decoration

Mancala boards are made in a variety of shapes, some of which immediately suggest a particular place of origin. The famous Asante stool shape, for example, can easily be recognised and attributed to West African artists, as can the hide-shaped boards typical of Uganda (see cat. nos 56-64). Folding boards in the shape of fish, etc. are common in Asia.

Schapiro (1953, p. 287) defines style as 'the constant form – and sometimes the constant elements, qualities, and expression – in the art of an individual or a group'. From an archaeological point of view, styles can be used to help localise and date artefacts, or to connect objects to certain cultures. The art-historical point of view stresses style as 'the meaningful expression through which the personality of the artist and the broad outlook of a group are visible' (Schapiro). Both the form of the object and its decoration are therefore relevant when attempting to define or analyse a style.

Thus the Ugandan boards are regarded as representing a single style in terms of their overall form, while the Sri Lankan boards constitute a stylistic group by virtue of their common decorative detail. Details can also recur within a particular form; for instance, the boat-shaped board with a stand often has a storage compartment in the base. The Asante stool form also shows variations:

A stool is composed of three parts, the base, the middle portion, and the top. . . . The middle has no normal shape. It is the portion which can be shaped into different patterns and symbols, and which shows the degree of skill of the carver and the status of the owner. . . . These figures in the middle section determine

17 Details of the carved interlace designs on a board from the Maldive Islands (*left*, cat. 86) and one from Sri Lanka (cat. 90) showing similarity of style. (Drawing: Hans Rashbrook)

0   5cm   0   5cm

18 Porcupine-design Asante stool with a 2 × 6 mancala board. Note the zigzag carving and the characteristic spines in the base. Akan, Gambia/Ghana (cat. 5).

what kind of stool it is, who can own it, and what it is worth in terms of money and culture. (Sarpong 1971)

Thus both the owner's status and the board's cultural and economic value can be assessed from its appearance: the prestigious 'porcupine' stool is clearly different from the 'twopenny' or poor man's stool. In this sense the artist defines the owner: by studying his work it becomes possible to determine the status of the board from its carvings. The overall shape, the parts of the stand, the elements of the board and the intricate carvings all have symbolic value. In addition to this general symbolism, individual carvings may also have specific symbolic meanings. For example, the top part of the Akan stool (see fig. 18), in this case the playing board, has a zigzag line between the two rows of holes with a clearly-defined snake's head at one end. This motif, known as 'the-snake-climbs-the-raffia-tree', symbolises a difficult undertaking.

In terms of its overall shape, then, a board may resemble a boat or a stool, a fish or a crocodile, an animal hide, a wheelbarrow or any one of a huge variety of other objects. Likewise, the playing holes, or cups, may

39

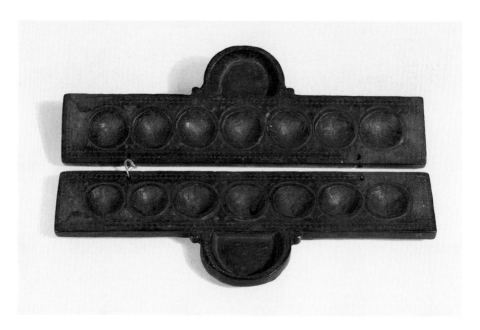

19 Folding board with handle containing end holes. Sri Lanka (cat. 96).

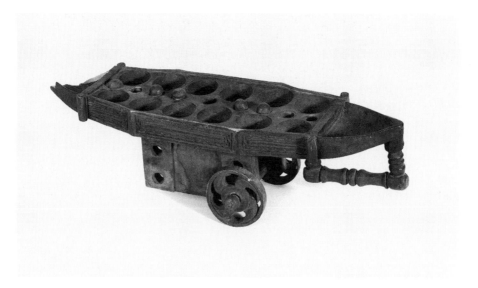

20 'Wheelbarrow' board. Sierra Leone (cat. 52).

21 Board from Sierra Leone with scallop-shaped outline. Little remains of the original base (cat. 45).

22 Block-shaped board with storage holes and end holes. Sierra Leone (cat. 47).

be round, square or bow-shaped; they may be arranged in parallel rows on a rectangular board, or the board may be shaped around them, creating a scalloped outline. Sometimes the holes form separate cups set upon a rectangular base: the animal-shaped board from Nigeria (cover illustration) has very distinctly separated cups. In the case of the Samburu board from Kenya, the light colour of the cups strengthens this effect of separation (see pl. 9).

In addition to the shape and disposition of the playing holes, the shape and placement of the end holes and/or storage holes is also significant. The symbolism of these features, found on many mancala boards around the world, is easily overstated. Although there is sometimes a meaning connected with these storage holes, boards with and without this feature coexist in the same region or even among the same players. Depending on the type of game, the storage hole is designed to keep captured seeds, to hold seeds yet to come into play, or to store seeds used to keep the score. Today it is also used as an ashtray during play or as a handle to carry the board.

The shape and history of each type is specific to its region and can help to determine the place of origin (see Walker 1986). Sri Lankan boards, for example, have square, centrally placed storage holes. A number of boards have a storage compartment hidden in the stand, demonstrating that storage holes and end holes can coexist, enabling captured seeds to be separated from stored seeds. In some games the end holes are used during play, as part of the game, and have special rules attached to them. Unfortunately, there are only a few cases in which we can be sure of the particular rules used to play on a specific board, since the number of variants possible is limited only by the number of holes and rows and not necessarily by the presence or absence of end holes.

Aesthetics

Roslyn Walker (1990) was the first to discuss mancala boards from an art-historical perspective. While she concentrated on sculptured mancala boards from Africa, this present study extends the discussion to include undecorated boards, not only from Africa but also from Asia and the

Caribbean. The boards from the British Museum collection provide the opportunity to observe the life cycle of a mancala board, which commences at the initial carving and (in the most extreme case) ends with its destruction, the changes that occur between modifying its aesthetic value in the process.

While mancala boards excavated in the earth are worn away or destroyed by the weather, wooden boards are worn through by the hands of the players throwing rock-hard pieces into the holes. Many rounds of the board are made before finishing a game, and one can easily wear out a couple of mancala boards within a lifetime. The hands shape the playing holes and smooth the surface through endless play. If a hand does not fit a hole, the fingers will groove and reshape it to create a perfectly sized hole from which the hand can take up the seeds as smoothly and elegantly as desired. As the holes become scarred with a progressive grooving, the board begins to disintegrate. Fortunately, storage in a museum halts this deterioration and preserves the material: the British Museum collection includes numerous examples of mended, broken, and worn-through pieces illustrating the successive stages in the life of a mancala board.

The playing qualities of a board are commonly judged by the size and the shape of the holes. As we have seen, even the weight of the board has some significance; the heavier the wood, the higher the durability and the playing quality of the board. There is thus a certain aesthetic quality to a popular playing board: the oldest boards acquire a wonderful shine from

23 Unfinished scallop-shaped board showing the initial design. Ghana (cat. 6).

playing and have much more charm than their newer, recently carved relatives. A playing board develops to accommodate the shape of a player's hand, but once this perfect shape has been acquired it will be destroyed by the playing process that created it. The personal board of Frederick 'The Lord Jesus' Jackman, a famous Barbados Warri player (author's collection) is a perfect example: the marks of the hands that shaped it are like an artist's signature (see fig. 25). Indeed, a player often has difficulty parting from his personal board.

The study of aesthetics in African and Asian art is a relatively recent discipline. Not until 1984 (Van Damme) was a doctoral study dedicated to the subject. Previous literature has concentrated on West African art in particular, using generalised concepts of beauty to appreciate, for instance, the famous Sande masks from Sierra Leone. The following appraisal represents an attempt to apply such criteria to mancala boards, using the broad headings of symmetry, moderation, clarity, delicacy, completeness, smoothness and novelty.

24 A 4 × 8 mancala board used for Bao. Note the shine of the playing holes. Tanzania (cat. 55).

25 Warri board previously used and owned by Frederick 'The Lord Jesus' Jackman. The deep grooves in the holes are the result of intensive play. Barbados, West Indies. Author's collection.

As far as symmetry is concerned, all mancala boards are symmetrical by nature; there is only one elaborately carved piece in the collection that does not conform to this principle (see fig. 26). Apart from this example, none of the boards has any asymmetrical features. Moderation implies that the boards should be neither too large nor too small and that all their features should be in due proportion. Again, apart from an odd example, the larger boards appear to have proportionately larger holes. In general, however, one could argue that playing holes with identical dimensions are to be preferred to those with disproportionate measurements. The least attractive example in this respect is the roughly carved tree trunk from Zambia with its many uneven holes (see cat. 67). In contrast, the boards from the Indian subcontinent and China are meticulously carved, with identical playing holes (see pl. 4).

Concepts of clarity and completeness are straightforward in the case of mancala boards. If the board is intact, its clarity and completeness in terms of its form are also satisfactory. Delicacy, however, is more difficult to determine. If delicacy is taken to refer to the amount of detail and the skill with which it has been executed, the detailed carvings on mancala boards should score highly in this respect. In terms of novelty, the boards incorporating animals in their overall shape can be quite extraordinary, like the crocodile-shaped board (fig. 27) and the ' bird cage' (fig. 28).

One of the boards in the British Museum collection has a carving of a

26 Sculptured board supported by rows of figures; identical figures are placed in reverse order on the other side. Benin, Nigeria (cat. 1).

27 A crocodile-shaped mancala board with a tin storage compartment. Nigeria (cat. 34).

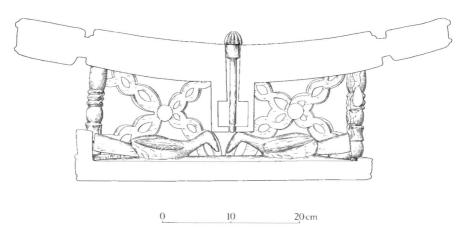

0   10   20 cm

28 Mancala board with an intricately carved openwork base incorporating a bird at either end. Sierra Leone (cat. 41). (Drawing: Hans Rashbrook)

PLATE 10 *(top)* A hand carved square-holed Warri board previously owned by the master player Benjamin White, who acquired it during the 1950s (cat. 105); *(bottom)* blue painted Warri board made by Ethelred Phillips (cat. 104). Both from Speightstown, Barbados.

PLATE 11 Heart-shaped folding board with iron handle and three stud feet on each side. The interior is coloured red. The small size of the playing holes would make the board difficult to use. India (cat. 76).

human head at one end (see title page). Judged according to the above criteria, it is clearly one of the finest boards in the collection. Not only is it one of the smoothest pieces, but its carved decoration is very accurate and precise. The outline and the dark colour of the wood combine to very fine effect, while the overall shine is almost unparalleled in any of the other boards. It represents an almost perfect blend of a work of art and a functional playing board.

As we have seen, the life cycle of a playing board consists of continuous physical change. The criteria postulated above make it possible to consider playing boards and even playing seeds in terms of their aesthetic value. In contrast, what makes a mancala board valuable to a discriminating player is its shine and the smoothness of its playing holes. When viewed from this perspective, it is reasonable to assert that even the humblest playing boards can indeed acquire a certain beauty at some stage in their life.

PLATE 12 (top) Beautifully carved and painted board with storage holes in the shape of tiny fish; (bottom) a fish-shaped board with red-painted scales and holes. India (cat. 79, 73).

CATALOGUE
OF THE
BRITISH MUSEUM
COLLECTION
OF MANCALA BOARDS

T HE catalogue is divided geographically into three sections: Africa, Asia and America. Within each section the boards are listed alphabetically by their country of origin and by the configuration of their holes: the number of rows followed by the number of holes per row and, if necessary, the number of end holes. Where necessary, the entries are further ordered according to their Museum registration number. Each entry also indicates the material, shape and dimensions of both boards and playing holes. All measurements are approximate and intended only to facilitate identification and further comparison. The size of the playing holes is divided into five classes: large (over 7.5 cm in diameter), hand-sized (6-7.5 cm), middle-sized (4-6 cm), small (2.5-4 cm) and minimal (less than 2.5 cm). A 'cup-shaped' hole or 'playing cup' resembles a hemisphere. A 'deep' hole is somewhat deeper; where a square hole is described as cup-shaped it resembles a cylinder cut lengthwise. End holes cannot be defined in such a precise way, since they are usually flat-bottomed and irregular in shape.

AFRICA

1 Benin (Nigeria), 2 × 6
Wood; board supported by twelve carved figures: a flute player, two kneeling women, a horseman, a monkey and a man facing sideways. Same figures on both sides, but in reverse sequence. Hand-sized playing cups. Finger grooves visible.
L. 60 cm, W. 23 cm, Ht 11.5 cm
Weight 2.4 kg
Af 1928,2-7.1 (fig. 26)

2 Chad, 4 × 4
Wood; square board on four square legs. Hand-sized square flat-bottomed playing holes.
L. 38.4 cm, W. 33.5 cm, Ht 9.5 cm
Weight 3.5 kg
Af 1911,12-14.77 (fig. 3)

3 Ethiopia, 3 × 6 (incomplete)
Cow dung; oval flat shape. Small playing holes; one hole missing at far corner.
L. 25 cm, W. 17 cm, Ht 2.2 cm
Weight 0.3 kg
Af 1893,7-15.19 (fig. 14)

4 Ethiopia, 3 × 6 + 2
Wood; two-piece board with leather hinges and relief carving around middle-sized playing cups. Hand-sized flat-bottomed end holes. 44 lead counters and 2 stone counters included.
First piece:
L. 20.9 cm, W. 18.9 cm, Ht 4.3 cm
Second piece:
L. 30.4 cm, W. 18.4 cm, Ht 3.9 cm
Weight 1.4 kg
Af 1893,7-15.17-18 (fig. 1)

29 Block-shaped
board. Sierra Leone
(cat. 48).

30 Hide-shaped
board. Uganda
(cat. 64).

31 Table-shaped
board. Uganda
(cat. 58).

5 Gambia (Ghana), 2 × 6 + 2
Wood; Asante stool with scallop-shaped
outline, the rows of holes separated by a
decorated rim. Porcupine design with
openwork stand. Middle-sized deep
flat-bottomed playing holes. Hand-sized
deep flat-bottomed end holes.
L. 54 cm, W. 17.2 cm, Ht 20.5 cm
Weight 3.4 kg
1947 Af 21.1 (fig. 18)

6 Ghana (unfinished)
Wood; stool-shaped. Porcupine design
on stand. The scallop-shaped upper
part may have been intended as a
mancala board.
L. 63.7 cm, W. 15 cm, Ht 20.3 cm
Weight 1.4 kg
1954 Af +23.3217 (fig. 23)

7 Ghana, 2 × 6
Wood; stool-shaped. Hand-sized deep
playing cups.
L. 47 cm, W. 18.7 cm, Ht 21 cm
Weight 2.4 kg
1954 Af +23.3023

8 Ghana, 2 × 6
Wood; red-pigmented folding board
with middle-sized flat-bottomed playing
holes.
L. 41.3 cm, W. 6.6 cm, Ht 5.7 cm
Weight 0.3 kg
1996 Af 15.1

9 Ghana, 2 × 6 + 2
Wood; Asante stool design with a rim
separating the rows of holes. The four
legs and base have geometric carvings.
Hand-sized flat-bottomed playing holes
and large end holes.

L. 67 cm, W. 15.7 cm, Ht.16.5 cm
Weight 1.6 kg
Af 1927,3-8.16

10 Ghana, 2 × 6 + 2
Wood; stool-shaped with storage
compartment in stand. Hand-sized
playing cups and end holes. 31 cowrie
shells included.
L. 63.3 cm, W. 16.6 cm, Ht 11.5 cm
Weight 2.4 kg
1996 Af 16.1

11 Guinea Bissau, 2 × 6 + 2
Wood; boat-shaped with middle-sized
smooth but crudely carved playing cups
and hand-sized end holes. 48 seeds
included.
L. 61 cm, W. 12.5 cm, Ht 7 cm
Weight 2.8 kg
1989 Af 5.3 (fig. 32)

12 Ivory Coast, 2 × 6 + 2
Wood: Asante stool with porcupine
design. A rim separates the rows of
holes. Hand-sized flat-bottomed playing
holes and end holes.
L. 63 cm, W. 16.5 cm, Ht 18 cm
Weight 2.0 kg
1948 Af 25.21

13 Ivory Coast, 2 × 6 + 2
Wood; block-shaped with four legs.
Extensive geometric carvings on the
sides. Middle-sized deep playing cups
and two hand-sized flat-bottomed end
holes supported by arms extending
from the base.
L. 76.5 cm, W. 14.5 cm, Ht 14.5 cm
Weight 3.0 kg
1954 Af 23.2932

32 Cat. 11.

14 Ivory Coast, 2 × 6 + 2
Wood; block-shaped with four legs. A
rim separates the rows of holes. Circle
motifs on the legs and on the arms
supporting the end holes. Middle-sized
deep playing cups and end holes.
Visible finger grooves.
L. 62 cm, W. 14.5 cm, Ht 19.5 cm
Weight 3.0 kg
1956 Af 27.21 (fig. 33)

15 Kenya, 2 × 12
Wood; scallop-shaped outline on a
flat base. Small irregular playing cups.
88 black counters in a leather pouch
included.
L. 71 cm, W. 10.5 cm, Ht 5.2 cm
Weight 1.6 kg
Af 1903,5-18.35

33 Cat. 14.

34 Cat. 19.

16 Kenya, 2 × 12
Wood; middle-sized playing cups. At
one end a cup has been pierced and
plugged with dark wood. Finger
grooves visible. 68 yellowish stones
included.
L. 71 cm, W. 19.5 cm, Ht 5 cm
Weight 2.9 kg
1991 Af 7.5a-b (pl. 9)

17 Kenya (Tanzania), 4 × 8
Wood; block-shaped. Middle-sized
deep flat-bottomed playing holes and
large diabolo-shaped houses in the
centre of the board.
L. 64 cm, W. 33 cm, Ht 6 cm
Weight 4.4 kg
Af 1922,6-9.14 (fig. 9)

18 Liberia (Sierra Leone), 2 × 6 + 2
Wood; boat-shaped with storage
compartment and carved stopper.
Chequerboard design carved on
support, pairs of relief-carved spiral
horns supporting the end holes. Hand-

sized playing cups and large drop-
shaped end holes. 40 counters included.
L. 67.5 cm, W. 14.5 cm, Ht 17 cm
Weight 1.5 kg
Af 1923,2-6.10

19 Malawi, 4 × 8 + 1
Wood; board supported on two legs
with rows of holes separated by a deep
groove. Zigzag carvings. Hand-sized
flat-bottomed playing holes with two
large square houses in the centre of the
board and one large end hole.
L. 117 cm, W. 44.1 cm, Ht 18.3 cm
Weight 12.5 kg
Af 1922,4-13.132 (fig. 34)

20 Malawi (Zambia), 4 × 8 + 4
Wood; hand-sized deep playing cups
with two large diabolo-shaped houses in
the centre of the board and four large
end holes.
L. 83.5 cm, W. 33.5 cm, Ht 16 cm
Weight 4.0 kg
Af 1896,12-23.1 (fig. 8)

21 Nigeria (Igala), 2 × 5 + 2
(incorporated in *Okega* shrine)
Wood; mancala board vertically placed
in central tier of shrine. Minimal square
flat-bottomed playing holes and middle-
sized triangular end holes.
Board: L. 24 cm, W. 5.2 cm, Ht 46 cm
1949 Af 46.192 (pl. 7)

22 Nigeria (Yoruba), 2 × 6
Wood; scallop-shaped outline with a
handle extending 4 cm from the board.
Lozenge motifs between the rows of
holes. Hand-sized playing cups.
L. 51 cm, W. 18.2 cm, Ht 4.2 cm
Weight 1.4 kg
Af 1934,5-7.1a-b

23 Nigeria (Yoruba), 2 × 6
Wood; scallop-shaped board on a flat
base with a 6.5 cm extension. Base
carved with notches. Hand-sized
smooth but crudely carved playing
cups.
L. 54 cm, W. 18 cm, Ht 5.5 cm

Weight 1.4 kg
Af 1938,10-10.10 (fig. 35)

24 Nigeria (Yoruba/Hausa), 2 × 6
Wood; animal-shaped with geometric
carvings painted in yellow and red with
black lozenge motifs. Scallop-shaped
rows of hand-sized playing cups.
L. 78 cm, W. 18.5 cm, Ht.18.5 cm
Weight 6.5 kg
1939 Af 7.31 (front cover)

25 Nigeria (Yoruba), 2 × 6
Wood; scallop-shaped board with two
2.3 cm extensions on one side. Hand-
sized playing cups with visible finger
grooves.
L. 53 cm, W. 16.5 cm, Ht 6 cm
Weight 1.7 kg
1939 Af 14.10

26 Nigeria (Yoruba), 2 × 6
Wood; scallop-shaped outline with a
9 cm projection in the shape of a
human head. Hand-sized deep and

35 Cat. 23.

36 Cat. 27.

smooth playing cups. Corner holes worn through by intensive play. Visible finger grooves.
L. 53 cm, W. 15 cm, Ht 4.8 cm
Weight 1.6 kg
1951 Af 5.1 (title page)

27 Nigeria, 2 × 6
Wood; blue, black and yellow coloured board supported by figures of a man holding a bird's tail and a woman. Projection carved in the shape of a human head. Hand-sized playing cups.
L. 63 cm, W. 21 cm, Ht 14.5 cm
Weight 2.4 kg
1954 Af 23.192 (fig. 36)

28 Nigeria (Yoruba), 2 × 6
Wood; coloured board with handle supported at the corners by four equestrian figures painted yellow, white, red, black and green and in the centre by a kneeling female figure holding a child. The figures have been carved separately and attached to the board with metal rods and nails. Large flat-bottomed playing holes.
L. 64 cm, W. 23 cm, Ht 53 cm
Weight 5.5 kg
1954 Af 23.193 (pl. 5)

29 Nigeria (Yoruba), 2 × 6
Wood; scallop-shaped outline on a stand with a 10 cm extension in the shape of a human head. Hand-sized playing cups with visible finger grooves. Two holes at far end worn through and repaired with scrap metal.
L. 55 cm, W. 18 cm, Ht 6 cm
Weight 1.3 kg
1954 Af 23.194

37 Cat. 30.

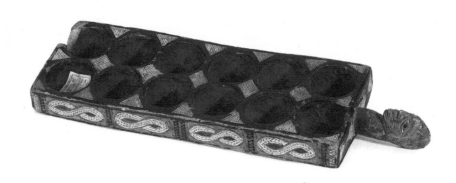

60

38 Cat. 33.

30 Nigeria (Yoruba), 2 × 6
Wood; coloured board with an 11 cm
extension in the shape of a human head
at one end. Geometric carvings
coloured red, white, black and yellow.
Hand-sized flat-bottomed playing holes.
L. 60 cm, W. 17 cm, Ht 5.5 cm
Weight 1.4 kg
1963 Af 13.13 (fig. 37)

31 Nigeria (Igala), 2 × 6 + 2
(incorporated in door)
Wood; polychrome door. Mancala
board vertically placed. Small playing
holes and small, square flat-bottomed
end holes.
Board: L. 27 cm, W. 8.3 cm, Ht 1.7 cm
1954 Af 23.1139 (pl. 6)

32 Nigeria, 2 × 6 + 2
Wood; block-shaped with stand.
Geometric carvings. Middle-sized,
squarish flat-bottomed playing holes
and large end holes.
L. 69.5 cm, W. 15 cm, Ht 8.5 cm
Weight 3.1 kg
1956 Af 7.1

33 Nigeria (Benin), 2 × 6 + 2
Wood; guilloche patterns carved on one
side, stylised heads of Portuguese men
on the other (see Walker 1990).
Middle-sized square flat-bottomed
playing holes and hand-sized flat-
bottomed end holes.
L. 64.5 cm, W. 13 cm, Ht 4.8 cm
Weight 0.7 kg
1957 Af 8.1 (fig. 38)

34 Nigeria, 2 × 6 + 2
Wood; crocodile-shaped board on stand
with tin storage compartment in the
centre. Extensive figurative and
geometric carvings. Middle-sized deep
and smooth flat-bottomed playing
holes, one large triangular end hole and
one oval end hole. 80 *Caesalpinia
Bonduc* seeds included.
L. 86 cm, W. 18 cm, Ht 19.3 cm
Weight 5 kg
1963 Af 17.1 (fig. 27)

35 Nigeria, 2 × 8
Wood; tree trunk. Large, roughly
carved playing holes.
L. 145 cm, W. 30 cm, Ht 22 cm

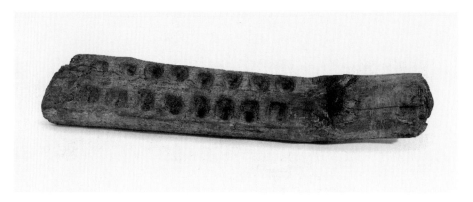

39 Cat. 35.

Weight 10.3 kg
1946 Af 18.208 (fig. 39)

36 Sierra Leone, 2 × 6 + 2
Wood; boat-shaped with scallop-shaped
playing board. Carved with lozenge and
rope motifs between the rows of holes
and on the sides of the end holes.
Middle-sized playing cups and large
square end holes. 24 *Caesalpinia Bonduc*
seeds included. Acquired in the 1860s.
L. 65.5 cm, W. 15 cm, Ht 12 cm
Weight 1.6 kg
Af 2186 (fig. 2)

37 Sierra Leone, 2 × 6 + 2
Wood; boat/block-shaped with storage
compartment in stand. Decorated with
geometric designs and circles carved out
of the stand. Middle-sized deep flat-
bottomed playing holes and large-sized
triangular end holes. Bottom of storage
compartment repaired with scrap metal.
L. 56.5 cm, W. 13 cm, Ht 15 cm
Weight 2.5 kg
Af 1921,3-11.2

38 Sierra Leone, 2 × 6 + 2
Wood; boat-shaped with stand. Storage
compartment in stand, originally with
human-headed stopper (now missing).
Similar carved head protrudes from end
of the 8.5 cm extension. Middle-sized
deep but irregular playing cups and
large triangular end holes.
L. 71 cm, W. 16 cm, Ht 19 cm
Weight 1.3 kg
Af 1935,1-14.4 (fig. 40)

39 Sierra Leone, 2 × 6 + 2
Wood; boat-shaped with two legs.
Middle-sized deep playing cups and
large triangular end holes.
L. 62.5 cm, W. 13 cm, Ht 9.8 cm
Weight 1.3 kg
Af 1936,11-2.1 (fig. 41)

40 Sierra Leone, 2 × 6 + 2
Wood; boat-shaped with stand.
Geometric designs on the stand and the
sides. Hand-sized deep flat-bottomed
playing holes and large triangular end
holes. End holes damaged.
L. 70 cm, W. 16.5 cm, Ht 15.5 cm

40 Cat. 38.

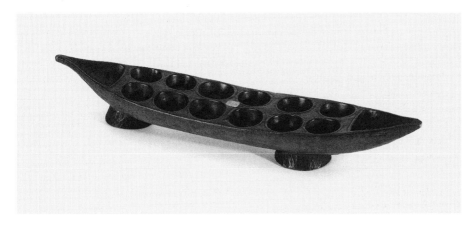

41 Cat. 39.

Weight 3.8 kg
1944 Af 4.191

41 Sierra Leone, 2 × 6 + 2
Wood; block-shaped. Elaborate
openwork stand carved with lathe and
ball motifs and two birds. Storage
compartment with drawer and peg.
Middle-sized deep playing cups and
large flat-bottomed end holes.
L. 63.5 cm, W. 15 cm, Ht 23 cm
Weight 3.4 kg
1950 Af 15.1.a-c (fig. 42)

42 Sierra Leone, 2 × 6 + 2
Wood; boat-shaped with storage
compartment in stand. Middle-sized
deep flat-bottomed playing holes and
large triangular flat-bottomed end holes.
L. 62 cm, W. 14.7 cm, Ht 16.5 cm
Weight 2.7 kg
1953 Af 25.9

43 Sierra Leone, 2 × 6 + 2
Wood; scallop-shaped board painted
blue-green and supported by four fixed
wheels (diameter 15.5 cm). Central
storage compartment with peg. Middle-
sized deep playing cups and hand-sized
end holes supported by arms extending
from the base. 36 cowrie shells
included.
L. 63 cm, W. 22.5 cm, Ht 25 cm
Weight 3.6 kg
1953 Af 25.10 (pl. 2)

44 Sierra Leone, 2 × 6 + 2
Wood; boat-shaped with storage
compartment in stand (stopper is
missing). Floral decoration between the
rows of holes. Supported at either end
by a standing figure with outstretched

arms attached to the board by
removable wooden dowels (one
missing). Middle-sized irregular flat-
bottomed playing holes and large
triangular end holes.
L. 69.5 cm, W. 16 cm, Ht.18.5 cm
Weight 2.1 kg
1954 Af +23.2930 (illus. p. 7)

45 Sierra Leone, 2 × 6 + 2
Wood; boat-shaped with damaged
stand and scallop-shaped board.
Storage compartment in stand is
extensively damaged. Middle-sized
playing cups and large triangular end
holes.
L. 71.5 cm, W. 12.5 cm, Ht 9 cm
Weight 1.5 kg
1954 Af +23.2931 (fig. 21)

46 Sierra Leone, 2 × 6 + 2
Wood; scallop-shaped board on stand.
Middle-sized playing cups and two
large end holes supported by arms
extending from the base.
L. 61.5 cm, W. 12.8 cm, Ht 18.7 cm
Weight 1.5 kg
1954 +23.2933

47 Sierra Leone, 2 × 6 +2
Wood; block-shaped with storage
compartment in stand. Bottom of the
storage compartment nailed to the
board. Elaborate carvings near end
holes and on stand. Ball motif between
the rows of holes. Middle-sized playing
cups and large end holes extending
from the board. 21 seeds included.
L. 61 cm, W. 14 cm, Ht 17 cm
Weight 3.1 kg
1954 +23.2934 (fig. 22)

PLATE 13 A craftsman from the Mikunguni Trade School, Zanzibar, using a chisel and
mallet to make mancala boards. On the bench in the foreground are two completed boards.
(Photo: Author)
PLATE 14 Warri being played by two masters in Speightstown, Barbados. (Photo: Author)

48 Sierra Leone, 2 × 6 + 2
Wood; block-shaped with openwork
stand. Lozenge motifs carved between
the rows of holes. Storage compartment
near one end hole supported by arms
extending from the base. Middle-size
deep playing cups and hand-sized end
holes.
L. 60 cm, W. 17.6 cm, Ht 16.5 cm
Weight 1.4 kg
1955 Af 2.1 (fig. 29)

49 Sierra Leone, 2 × 6 + 2
Wood; boat-shaped board on stand.
Geometric designs. Hand-sized playing
cups and large-sized triangular end
holes. One end hole broken off.
L. 63.3 cm, W. 16 cm, Ht 11.3 cm
Weight 1.7 kg
1956 Af 10.4

50 Sierra Leone, 2 × 6 + 2
Wood; boat-shaped board with storage
compartment in stand. Spiral orna-
ments and geometric designs. Middle-
sized playing cups and large triangular
end holes. Counters included in stand.
L. 61 cm, W. 13.5 cm, Ht 16 cm
Weight 1.6 kg
1956 Af 10.5 (fig. 43)

51 Sierra Leone, 2 × 6 + 2
Wood; boat-shaped board resting on
two legs with carved pig supporting the
centre. Painted black. Cross-hatched
patterns carved on the sides. Middle-
sized flat-bottomed playing holes and
large triangular end holes. 54 seeds
included.
L. 54.5 cm, W. 12.5 cm, Ht 21.5 cm
Weight 1.4 kg
1958 Af 13.12 (fig. 44)

52 Sierra Leone, 2 × 6 + 2
Wood; boat-shaped, supported by four
functional wheels (two missing).
Storage compartment in stand with peg
and additional false pegs. Handle
carved with lathe motif. Chain motif on
the sides. Middle-sized flat-bottomed
playing holes and large triangular flat-
bottomed end holes (one damaged).
L. 63.5 cm, W. 16.5 cm, Ht 18.4 cm
Weight 2.1 kg
1968 Af 14.1 (fig. 20)

53 Sierra Leone (Nigeria), 2 × 6 + 2
Wood; boat-shaped board with stand.
Middle-sized roughly carved playing
cups and large end holes.
L. 65.5 cm, W. 13.5 cm, Ht 9.6 cm
Weight 3.4 kg
1996 Af 17.1

54 Somalia, 4 × 8
Wood; board with metal bolts in the
side. Middle-sized flat-bottomed
playing holes and two middle-sized
square houses in centre of board. One
hole near the centre is worn through.
L. 55.6 cm, W. 25.2 cm, Ht 5.7 cm
Weight 4.5 kg
Af 1935,11-8.275

55 Tanzania, 4 × 8
Wood; hand-sized playing cups and two
hand-sized square houses in the centre
of the board. 100 *Caesalpinia Bonduc*
seeds included.
L. 60.6 cm, W. 32.4 cm, Ht 4.5 cm
Weight 4.5 kg
1990 Af 8.1 (fig. 24)

56 Uganda, 4 × 8
Wood; table-shaped board with

PLATE 15 *(from top to bottom, left to right)* The fruit of the *Caesalpinia Bonduc*; the inside of one
of the seeds; a selection of *Caesalpinia Bonduc* seeds showing variations in colour; seeds used in
Antigua; seeds showing variations in shape and size. (Author's collection)
PLATE 16 Calculating changes: one of the master players during the Bao championships in
Zanzibar, 1994. (Photo: Author)

42 Cat. 41.

43 Cat. 50.

44 Cat. 51.

45 Cat. 59.

pedestal. Large square flat-bottomed
playing holes. 152 *Caesalpinia Bonduc*
seeds included.
L. 102 cm, W. 58 cm, Ht 45 cm
Weight 7.8 kg
Af 1919, Loan 4.56 (fig. 11)

57 Uganda, 4 × 8
Wood; table-shaped board with square
smooth middle-sized flat-bottomed
playing holes.
L. 50 cm, W. 11.5 cm, Ht 30.5 cm
Weight 1.3 kg
Af 1933,11-20.32

58 Uganda, 4 × 8
Wood; table-shaped board, painted
black. Hand-sized squarish flat-
bottomed playing holes.
L. 56 cm, W. 33.5 cm, Ht 21 cm
Weight 3.1 kg
1952 Af 7.211 (fig. 31)

59 Uganda, 4 × 8
Wood; hide-shaped board with middle-
sized squarish flat-bottomed playing
holes. 64 seeds included.
L. 51 cm, W. 31 cm, Ht 3 cm
Weight 1.3 kg
1952 Af 7.212 (fig. 45)

60 Uganda, 4 × 8 +1
Wood; hide/table-shaped. Middle-sized
irregular flat-bottomed playing holes
and a hand-sized deep flat-bottomed
end hole.
L. 62.5 cm, W. 32 cm, Ht 7 cm
Weight 2.3 kg
1954 Af +23.2923

61 Uganda, 4 × 8 +1
Wood; hide-shaped board with 6 cm
extension. Middle-sized square playing
cups.
L. 46 cm, W. 35 cm, Ht 3 cm

Weight 1.5 kg
1954 Af +23.2924

62 Uganda, 4 × 8
Wood; hide-shaped board with 3 cm
extension. Middle-sized square and
irregular playing cups.
L. 44 cm, W. 27 cm, Ht 3.3 cm
Weight 1.3 kg
1962 Af 17.78

63 Uganda, 4 × 8
Wood; hide-shaped board with 6.5 cm
extension. Middle-sized square and
irregular playing cups. 49 seeds
included.
L. 48 cm, W. 24 cm, Ht 3.7 cm
Weight 0.7 kg
1973 Af 29.3

64 Uganda, 4 × 8
Wood; hide-shaped board with 4.5 cm
extension. Hand-sized square and
irregular playing cups.
L. 48.5 cm, W. 35.5 cm, Ht 3.8 cm
Weight 1.4 kg
1979 Af 1.2481 (fig. 30)

65 Zaire, 3 × 3 + 2 (incorporated in
statue)
Wood; King Shyaam aMbul aNgoong,
regarded as the founder of the Kuba
kingdom. Cowries and interlace
patterns carved in relief. Minimal
playing cups and small end holes.
Board: L. 11.2 cm, W. 5.4 cm, Ht 3.5
cm
Af 1909,12-10.1 (fig. 10)

66 Zaire (Uganda), 4 × 8
Wood; hide-shaped board with 4.5 cm
extension. Middle-sized, irregular flat-

bottomed playing holes. 48 seeds
included.
L. 51 cm, W. 28 cm, Ht 2.5 cm
Weight 1.0 kg
Af 1904,6-22.2

67 Zambia, 2 × 8 + 2
Wood; tree trunk. Hand-sized squarish
flat-bottomed playing holes with two
enlarged holes in the middle of the
board and two large flat-bottomed end
holes. Possibly originally a 2 × 9 board
altered by merging two holes in the
centre of the rows.
L. 118 cm, W. 15.5 cm, Ht 10.5 cm
Weight 5.6 kg
1972 Af 14.244

68 Zambia, 4 × 8
Corrugated iron with dents forming
middle-sized playing holes. Brand name
Ysker/Iscor visible on reverse.
L. 71.7 cm, W. 28.6 cm, Ht 2 cm
Weight 1 kg
1972 Af 14.246 (fig. 16)

69 Zambia, 4 × 8 + 1
Wood; tree trunk. Large square playing
holes and one large square end hole.
L. 112 cm, W. 43 cm, Ht 9 cm
Weight 16.8 kg
1972 Af 14.245 (fig. 15)

70 Zambia, 4 × 8 + 1
Wood; hand-sized flat-bottomed
playing holes with two hand-sized
square houses in the centre of the board
and one large end hole.
L. 81.5 cm, W. 29 cm, Ht 5.5 cm
Weight 6.3 kg
1993 Af 13.12a

ASIA

71 China, 2 × 7 + 2
Wood; folding board lacquered in
black, gold and red. Middle-sized
playing cups with middle-sized tear-
shaped end holes.
L. 49 cm, W. 13.3 cm, Ht 6 cm
(folded)
Weight 0.75 kg
As 1931,5-5.1 (pl. 4)

72 India, 2 × 7 (incomplete)
Ivory; rectangular single piece (1 × 7)
of two-piece folding board. Carved
braid motif. Small playing cups.
L. 35 cm, W. 7 cm, Ht 2.8 cm
Weight 1.3 kg
As 1897,3-18.5 (fig. 13)

73 India, 2 × 7
Wood; fish-shaped folding board
painted red inside. Elaborately carved
with green head and red scales. Middle-
sized playing cups.
L. 49.5 cm, W. 12 cm, Ht 5.8 cm
(folded)
Weight 2.1 kg
1996 As 30.5 (pl. 12, bottom)

74 India, 2 × 7
Wood; ridged folding board with small
playing cups.
L. 34.8 cm, W. 6.8 cm, Ht 7 cm
(folded)
Weight 0.7 kg
1996 As 30.6

75 India, 2 × 7
Wood; ridged folding board with
middle-sized playing cups.

L. 38 cm, W. 7.2 cm, Ht 6.5 cm
(folded)
Weight 0.7 kg
1996 As 30.7

76 India, 2 × 7 + 1
Wood; heart-shaped folding board with
six legs. Copper alloy parts attached.
Red-coloured small playing cups and
large shallow end hole.
L. 37.5 cm, W. 16 cm, Ht 6.4 cm
(unfolded)
Weight 0.9 kg
1996 As 31.1 (pl. 11)

77 India, 2 × 7 + 2
Wood; fish-shaped folding board
painted black with small playing cups
and middle-sized fish-shaped end holes.
Inscription on the outside.
L. 47 cm, W. 12.2 cm, Ht 5.2 cm
(folded)
Weight 1.9 kg
1996 As 30.1 (fig. 46, top)

78 India, 2 × 7 + 2
Wood; fish-shaped folding board with
middle-sized playing cups and middle-
sized square flat-bottomed houses.
L. 53.5 cm, W. 11.5 cm, Ht 8.2 cm
(folded)
Weight 3.0 kg
1996 As 30.2 (fig. 46, bottom)

79 India, 2 × 7 + 2
Wood; fish-shaped folding board
painted white, red and yellow outside
and green inside. Middle-sized playing
cups painted with flowers inside and
large fish-shaped flat-bottomed end
holes painted with red and yellow scales
inside.

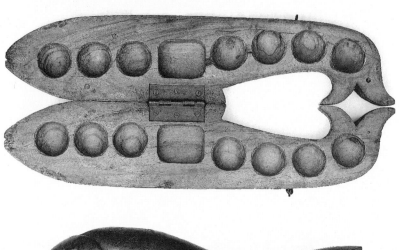

46 Cat. 77-8.

L. 51.5 cm, W. 17.3 cm, Ht 10.2 cm
(folded)
Weight 3.0 kg
1996 As 30.3 (pl. 12, top)

80 India, 2 × 7 + 2
Wood; fish-shaped folding board
decorated with linear designs. Middle-
sized playing cups and end holes.
L. 41 cm, W. 13 cm, Ht 5.4 cm
(folded)
Weight 2.0 kg
1996 As 30.4

81 India, 2 × 7 + 2
Wood; cube-shaped double-folding

board with drawer and lock. Middle-
sized playing cups and large-sized
shallow end holes.
L. 49 cm, W. 14.4 cm, Ht 9 cm
(unfolded)
Weight 2.3 kg
1996 As 30.8

82 Indonesia (Java), 2 × 3 + 2
Wood; board in the shape of two
golden dragons/snakes with red tongues;
supported on four legs. Small flat-
bottomed playing holes and middle-
sized flat-bottomed end holes alternately
coloured green and red. Colouring
damaged.

L. 45 cm, W. 9.5 cm, Ht 12.5 cm
Weight 1.8 kg
1997 As 7.1 (pl. 3)

83 Indonesia (Java), 2 × 7 + 2
Wood; monkey-faced figures with red
lips, white faces and blue and green
clothing holding sides of polychrome
board. Middle-sized playing cups and
large end holes.
L. 70.7 cm, W. 16 cm, Ht 22 cm
Weight 3.2 kg
1997 As 7.3 (back cover)

84 Indonesia (Java), 2 × 9 + 2
Wood; red and gold painted board in
the form of a stylised dragon supported
on four legs with upright animal-head
terminals. Flower motifs. Middle-sized
flat-bottomed playing holes and end
holes.
L. 79 cm, W. 15.5 cm, Ht 26.2 cm
Weight 2.5 kg
1997 As 7.2 (pl. 1)

85 Malaysia, 2 × 7 + 2
Wood; boat-shaped board with small
playing holes and hand-sized triangular
end holes.
L. 53 cm, W. 10.5 cm, Ht 5 cm
Weight 0.6 kg
As 1886,12-13.58

86 Maldive Islands, 2 × 8 + 2
Wood; board supported by two legs.
Incised and inlaid floral and interlace
motifs. Middle-sized flat-bottomed
playing holes and large semicircular end
holes.
L. 65 cm, W. 10.7 cm, Ht 7.1 cm
Weight 2.5 kg
As 1893,11-23.98 (fig. 47)

87 Maldive Islands, 2 × 8 + 2
Wood; board supported by two legs.
Middle-sized machine-made flat-
bottomed playing holes and large end
holes. 81 counters included.
L. 70 cm, W. 12 cm, Ht 4.7 cm

47 Cat. 86.

Weight 2.2 kg
1981 As 20.125a-b

88 Maldive Islands, 2 × 8 + 2
Wood; middle-sized roughly carved
flat-bottomed playing holes and large
end holes. 85 counters included.
L. 80 cm, W. 13 cm, Ht 7 cm
Weight 2.5 kg
1981 As 20.126a-b

89 Sri Lanka, 2 × 7 + 2
Wood; four legs. Carved with braid
motif. Small playing cups and middle-
sized square end holes.
L. 39 cm, W. 8 cm, Ht 6.5 cm
Weight 1.6 kg
As 1898,7-3.12

90 Sri Lanka, 2 × 7 + 2
Wood; four legs, of which two are
damaged. Carved with braid motif.
Small playing cups and hand-sized
square end holes set between the rows.
L. 38.5 cm, W. 20.6 cm, Ht 7 cm
Weight 2.4 kg
As 1898,7-3.13

91 Sri Lanka, 2 × 7 + 2
Wood; four leg sockets (legs missing).
Carved with braid motif. Small playing
holes and hand-sized square end holes
set between the rows of holes.
L. 39 cm, W. 22 cm, Ht 3 cm
Weight 1.3 kg
As 1898,7-3.14

92 Sri Lanka, 2 × 7 + 2
Wood; four legs. Carved with braid

48 Cat. 92.

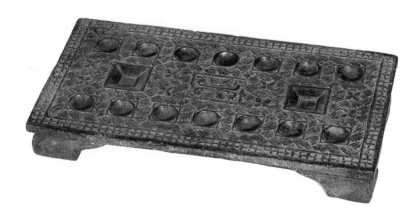

49 Cat. 94.

motif. Minimal cups and middle-sized square end holes set between the rows of holes.
L. 34.8 cm, W. 18.5 cm, Ht 5.4 cm
Weight 1.1 kg
As 1898,7-3.16 (fig. 48)

93 Sri Lanka, 2 × 7 + 2
Wood; carved with braid motif. Small cups and middle-sized square end holes set between the rows of holes.
L. 28.3 cm, W. 16.9 cm, Ht 3 cm
Weight 0.9 kg
As 1898,7-3.17

94 Sri Lanka, 2 × 7 + 2
Wood; carvings of peacocks. Minimal cups and small square end holes set between the rows of holes.
L. 30 cm, W. 15.5 cm, Ht 6.3 cm

Weight 1.3 kg
As 1898,7-3.18 (fig. 49)

95 Sri Lanka, 2 × 7 + 2
Wood; cuboid double folding board converts into a board with two legs and a stand. Minimal cups and small square end holes.
L. 36.5 cm, W. 12.5 cm, Ht 8 cm (unfolded)
L. 12.5 cm, W. 14.5 cm, Ht 15.3 cm (folded)
Weight 1.7 kg
As 1898,7-3.19 (fig. 12)

96 Sri Lanka, 2 × 7 + 2
Wood; folding board with handle containing end holes. Minimal cups and small end holes on the long side of the board.

L. 24 cm, W. 8.2 cm, Ht 1.7 cm
Weight 0.25 kg
As 1898,7-3.20 (fig.19)

97 Sri Lanka, 2 × 7 + 2
Wood; fish-shaped folding board with
minimal cups and middle-sized square
end holes.
L. 36.5 cm, W. 7.5 cm, Ht 6 cm
(folded)
Weight 0.38 kg
As 1898,7-3.21 (fig. 50)

98 Sri Lanka, 2 × 7 + 3
Wood; four legs. Carved with braid
motif. Minimal cups with two small and
one middle-sized square end holes set
between the rows of holes.
L. 32 cm, W. 18.9 cm, Ht 5.4 cm
Weight 0.76 kg
As 1898,7-3.15

99 Sri Lanka, 2 × 7 + 4
Wood; fish-shaped folding board.
Hinges missing. Minimal cups and
small square end holes, one set between
the rows of holes.
L. 40 cm, W. 13.2 cm, Ht 3.5 cm
(folded)
Weight 1.1 kg
As 1898,7-3.22

100 Syria, 2 × 7
Wood; folding board with hand-sized
machine-made playing cups.
L. 61.5 cm, W. 8.3 cm, Ht 5.6 cm
Weight 2.7 kg
1996 As 33.1 (fig. 4, top)

101 Syria, 2 × 7
Wood; varnished folding board, inlaid
with pieces of mother-of-pearl. Hand-
sized machine-made playing cups.
L. 62 cm, W. 8.0 cm, Ht 6.6 cm

50 Cat. 97.

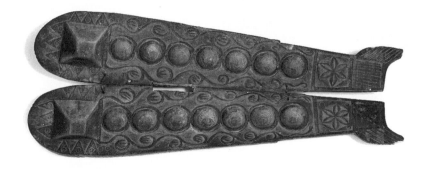

Weight 2.5 kg
1996 As 33.2 (fig. 4, centre)

102 Syria, 2 × 7
Wood; varnished folding board with
hand-sized machine-made playing cups.
L. 51.7 cm, W. 15.7 cm, Ht 5.3 cm
Weight 0.9 kg
1996 As 33.3 (fig. 4, bottom)

AMERICA

103 Antigua, 2 × 6 + 2
Wood; large deep roughly-carved flat-
bottomed playing holes and large end
holes.
L. 77.5 cm, W. 30.5 cm, Ht 5.7 cm
Weight 5.5 kg
Am 1936.10-8.1 (fig. 7)

104 Barbados, 2 × 6
Wood; painted blue. Hand-sized
machine-made flat-bottomed playing
holes. Made by Warri master Ethelred
Phillips.
L. 60.5 cm, W. 18.5 cm, Ht 4.5 cm
Weight 2.9 kg
1996 Am 17.1 (pl. 10, bottom)

105 Barbados, 2 × 6
Wood; hand-sized roughly carved
square playing holes. Previously owned
by Warri master Benjamin White.
L. 63.6 cm, W. 18.5 cm, Ht 4.7 cm
Weight 3.2 kg
1996 Am 17.2 (pl. 10, top)

BIBLIOGRAPHY

● ●

Abiodun, R., Drewal, H. J., and Pemberton, J., 1994. *The Yoruba Artist: New Theoretical Perspectives on African Arts*, Washington

Allis, L. V., van den Herik, H. J., and van der Meulen, M., 1991. 'Databases in Awari', in D. Beal and D. Levy (eds), *Heuristic Programming in Artificial Intelligence, 2: The Second Computer Olympiad*, Chichester, pp. 73-86

Ayomíke, J. O. S., 1993. *Benin and Warri: Meeting Points in History: The Itsekiri Perspective*, Warri, Nigeria

Ballou, K., 1978. *Règles et Stratégies du Jeu d'Awale*, Abidjan-Dakar-Lomé

Barnes, R. H., 1975. 'Mancala in Kédang: a structural test', in *Bijdragen tot de Taal-, Land- en Volkenkunde* 131: 1, The Hague

Béart, C., 1955. *Jeux et Jouets de l'Ouest Africain*, Dakar

Bell, R. C., 1960. *Board and Table Games from Many Civilizations*, Oxford

Boone, S. A., 1986. *Radiance from the Waters: Ideals of Feminine Beauty in Mende Art*, New Haven

Culin, S., 1893. 'Exhibition of games at Columbian Exposition', *Journal of American Folklore* 6, pp. 205-27

Deledicq, A., and Popova, A., 1977. *Wari et Solo: Le Jeu de Calcul Africain*, Paris

Eagle, V. A., 1995. 'On some newly described mancala games from Yunnan Province, China, and the definition of a genus in the family of mancala games', in de Voogt 1995b

de Flacourt, E., 1658. *Histoire de la Grande Isle Madagascar*, Paris

Herskovits, M. J., 1932. 'Wari in the New World', *Journal of the Royal Anthropological Institute* 62, pp. 23-39

Huizinga, J., 1938. *Homo Ludens: Proeve ener bepaling van het spelelement der Cultur*, Groningen

Murray, H. J. R., 1952. *A History of Board Games other than Chess*, London

National Museums of Tanzania, 1971. *How to Play Bao?*, Dar es Salaam

N'Guessan Assandé, G., 1986. 'L'apprentissage de l'Awélé: étude du processus d'acquisition des tactiques et stratégies', conference paper presented at the Colloque de Cerisy-la-Salle (June)

Nsimbi, M. B., 1968. *Omweso: A Game People Play in Uganda*, University of California African Studies Center Occasional Paper 6, Berkeley

Odeleye, A. O., 1977. *Ayo: A Popular Yoruba Game*, Ibadan

Retschitzki, J., 1990. *Stratégies des Joueurs d'Awélé*, Paris

Russ, L., 1984. *Mancala Games*, Michigan

Santos Silva, E. R., 1995. *Jogos de Quadrícula do tipo Mancala com especial incidência nos praticados em Angola*, Lisbon

Sarpong, P., 1971. *The Sacred Stools of the Akan*, Ghana

Schapiro, M., 1953. 'Style', in A. L. Kroeber (ed.), *Anthropology Today*, Chicago, pp. 287-312

Townshend, P., 1977a. 'Les jeux de mankala au Zaïre, au Ruanda et au Burundi', *Les Cahiers du CEDAF* 3:1

Townshend, P., 1977b. 'Mankala games', *International Committee on Urgent Anthropological and Ethnological Research* 19, pp. 47-54

Townshend, P., 1979. *Anthropological Perspectives on Bao (Mankala) Games*, University of Nairobi Institute of African Studies Paper 114, Nairobi

Townshend, P., 1986. 'Games in culture: a contextual analysis of the Swahili board game and its relevance to variation in African mankala', Ph.D. thesis, University of Cambridge

Van Damme, W., 1984. 'Descriptief en analytisch overzicht van het onderzoek naar Negro-Afrikaanse esthetische opvattingen', Ph. D. thesis, Rijksuniversiteit Gent

Van Damme, W. 1987. *A Comparative Analysis Concerning Beauty and Ugliness in Sub-Saharan Africa*, Rijksuniversiteit Gent Africana Gandensia 4, Ghent

Von Neumann, J., and Morgenstern, O., 1944. *Theory of Games and Economic Behavior*, Princeton

de Voogt, A. J., 1995a. *Limits of the Mind: Towards a Characterisation of Bao Mastership*, Leiden

de Voogt, A. J. (ed.), 1995b. *New Approaches to Board Games Research: Asian Origins and Future Perspectives*, IIAS Working Papers, Series 3, Leiden

Walker, R. A., 1986. 'A sculptured mancala gameboard terminating in a carved human head from Liberia in the Barbier-Mueller Museum', *Bulletin [of the] Association des Amis du Musée Barbier-Mueller* 32, pp. 1-6

Walker, R. A., 1990. 'Sculptured mancala gameboards of Sub-Saharan Africa', Ph.D. thesis, Indiana University

INDEX